Pick It Up!

Written by Sasha Morton
Illustrated by Lorian Dean

RISING STARS

I can get it.
Plop!

No! I will get it.

I can pick it up.

No! I will pick it up.

I can get the bag.

No! I will get the bag.

I can put it back.

No! I will put it back.
Slip

I can pack the bag.

I will pick it up!
Plop!
Plop!
Snap!

Talk about the story

Ask your child these questions:

1 What did the girl try to do on the first page of the story?

2 Why did the cakes fall off the trolley?

3 What did the shop assistant say on the last page?

4 Why did the food land on the floor at the end of the story?

5 Which type of fruit would you have chosen to buy?

6 Do you like shopping in the supermarket?
Why or why not?

Can your child retell the story in their own words?